Red Handed

MIKE WILSON

Lee hates Saturdays.

Saturdays are boring.
There's nothing to do.

There's nothing on telly,
just sport and old films
and horse racing.

Mum's at work.
Dad's out with his metal detector.
Sharon's upstairs,
doing something.

His mum left Lee some jobs to do.
But he hasn't done them yet.

And so there's nothing else to do
but watch this stupid horse
win this stupid race.

Then Rob comes home.
Robert is Lee's big brother.
He's nearly twenty.

He looks terrible.
He looks as if he hasn't slept for days.

He goes upstairs,
and soon Lee hears water splashing.

Rob still has a bed in the house,
but they don't see that much of him.
They don't really know where he goes,
or what he gets up to.

Then Rob comes down again,
in clean clothes.

He gets on the phone.

"Can I speak to Detective Inspector Martin?
...Yes, this is Rob Warner...yes, Robert.
When can I have my car back?
Yes, the mini..."

Rob listens to the policeman
for about two minutes.
Then he slams the phone down
without another word.

Sharon comes downstairs.
"How come you've got a car, Rob?" she asks.
"You haven't passed your test..."

"I haven't got a car," says Rob.
"Not any more."

And he swears at the policeman.

Robert explains:
"First – the copper says
I parked somewhere I shouldn't!

"I only left it there two minutes!

"Then – they took the car away
and I've got to pay ninety-five quid
to get it back!

"Now – he's saying I had no tax,
no insurance, no MOT..."

"And no driving licence,"
sister Sharon added,
"don't forget that!"

"I can drive, Sharon!" Rob shouts,
"I can drive better than most people
who have passed their test.

"Anyway there's this guy I know.
He'll sell me a car.
You got to have wheels!

"If you haven't got wheels, you're nothing.
You might as well be dead!"

Rob stands still for a second,
staring at nothing.

Then he seems to see Lee
for the first time since he came in.

Lee is watching his big brother,
waiting for something to happen.

Rob says:
"Do you know what twoccing is, Lee?"

Lee thinks he knows, but he isn't sure,
so he says nothing.

Rob goes on:
"It stands for
Taking...
Without...the
Owner's...
Consent.

"It's nicking.
Nicking cars.

"Twoccing.
That's what they call it now."

Again, Lee can't think of anything to say.

He waits for Rob to carry on,
but Rob seems to have stopped again.

Suddenly, Rob says:
"Come on, kid. Get your coat.
Let's go and see mum!"

They go out, and cross the road,
past the taxi on its bricks.

Ifty is lying under it,
talking to himself, softly,
half in English, half in Urdu.

The two brothers go over to Hussain's.

They know Hussain is not there.
He's always out at this time.
So it's a good time to try out their plan.

They go in.

Their mum is standing talking to old Mrs Butler,
but the old lady picks up her bag
and shuffles slowly to the door
when the boys come in.

Lucky for them.

"Dear oh dear," says Jackie,
looking at her eldest son.
"Look what the cat dragged in!
What's up, Robbie,
did you run out of clean clothes?"

"I need a word, Mum,"
Robert says.
"In private."

If it's about lending you some you-know-what,"
says Jackie,
"the answer's no!"

Rob leads her off to the far end of the shop,
about thirty feet away,
down by the veg.

Lee, left alone at the counter,
stands and watches them go.

There's nobody else in the shop,
but he knows Mrs Hussain is in the next room.
He can hear her television.

He will have to be quick.

The way Rob stands,
at the back of the shop,
mum's back is to the counter.

Lee waits.

Then suddenly
he darts behind the counter.

He grabs cigarettes, and sweets
from the back wall.
He takes anything
that he can jam into his pockets,
anything that won't be seen under his jacket.

But he's careful:
he doesn't take the last one of anything,
so his mum won't spot a gap.

All this takes about six seconds.

Lee is just stepping round,
back to the other side of the counter,
when the door of the shop opens.

He is still carefully hiding
one last packet of sweets
in his jacket.

Lee is caught red-handed
by whoever is coming in.
He stops dead.
He can't move.

Lee's mum hears the bell on the door,
and looks back up the shop.

She sees Lee standing face-to-face
with Danny Davenport,
his friend from round the corner.

Lee and Danny are in the same class
at school together.

Jackie comes from the back of the shop.
"Now then, young man," she asks
"what can we do for you?

Lee moves away from the counter
as his mum comes near.

He's looking very closely
at some plastic clothes pegs
on a card near the door of the shop.

"Er..." Danny begins,
"My mum sent me over..."

But then he stops.
He turns to look at Lee.

The back of Lee's neck is all red.

Jackie says: "Come on, Danny!
Have you forgotten
what your mum sent you for?"

Rob comes over and stands over Danny.
He doesn't say anything.
He doesn't need to.

His look is enough.

Jackie is still talking:

"Run back home and ask her again.
Tell her what a big daft thing you are!"

Then Danny pipes up:

"She wants two tins of rice pudding!
I didn't forget.

"I was just thinking –
it's a shame
I haven't got enough money
to buy a few sweets as well..."

He looks up at Rob, then back again at Lee.

"'Cos I like sweets, I do..." he says, evenly.

Danny pays for the tins for his mum,
and turns to go.

He stops by Lee in the doorway,
and says:

"I'll see you Monday, then.
At school."

"Yes," says Lee.

Then Lee seems to have a bright idea.
"I know," he goes,
"I'll bring you some sweets in, if you like..."

"Yes," goes Danny.
"That will be nice."

And then he's gone,
trotting up the road
with his two tins of rice pudding.

The way he dances off home,
you'd think he'd won the pools,

or peeped into the lion's den
and escaped with a tube of Smarties.